HÄGAR
THE HORRIBLE

Makes An Entrance

by
Dik Browne

ATTICA
PUBLICATIONS

First published 1988 by Attica Publications.

Attica Limited,
DLM House,
Edinburgh Way,
Harlow, Essex, CM20 2HL
England.

ISBN 1 85176 172 1

Printed in Hong Kong

VOFF!

...BUT IT DOESN'T SHOW THE DIRT AS MUCH AND WE CAN STILL USE THE SIDEBOARD — WITH A NEW COVER, OF COURSE...

GOTCHA.

11-30

DIK BROWNE

IT TOPPLED BIG CHIMNEYS
AND UPROOTED TREES

IT WAS FELT IN ASIA AND
KENSINGTON, TOO
AND EVEN ON THE OCEAN BLUE

AND IT FINALLY MADE A PALM
TREE SWAY
IN BOONA-BOONA FAR AWAY

1-18

AND MOVED A NATIVE WIFE
TO SAY:

NOW WHERE DID
YOU CATCH
THAT?!

ACHOO

DIK BROWNE

YOU REST THOSE POOR TIRED FEET IN THIS EASY CHAIR.

A LITTLE LIBATION WILL HELP UNRAVEL THOSE OLD NERVES.

NOW, YOU SIT THERE AND RELAX AND I'LL GET YOU A REAL NICE DINNER.

1-25

DIK BROWNE

WHAT A DAY!! FIRST I LOSE THE BATTLE...THEN THE BOOTY...I GET ZAPPED SIX TIMES...FINALLY MAKE IT HOME, ONLY TO FIND THAT MY WIFE HAS GONE NUTS!

BOY! WHAT A BUSINESS FOR A NICE BOY LIKE ME TO END UP IN!

EVERY PART OF MY BODY ACHES — INCLUDING MY SHIELD!

YOU THINK IT'S EASY BEING A VIKING?!

TRAVELING ALL THE TIME...

BURP!

IN ALL KINDS OF WEATHER...

LONDON

IF IT DOESN'T GET TOSSED OUT—THINGS ARE OKAY

OH—OH!

PLINK!

DIK BROWNE
8-8

PONK!

BOK!

I'D BETTER GIVE HER A LITTLE TIME TO COOL OFF...

PING!

PLOP!

O THE YULE-LOG TIME OF YEAR! PRESENT-GIVING TIME IS HERE.

FRIENDS, OLD AND NEW, I NOW SALUTE AND PASS AROUND A LITTLE LOOT.

FOR HELGA, MY LOVE, THESE GIFTS I GOT A GOWN, A RING, A NOODLE POT.

A BOOK FOR HAMLET A COMB FOR HONI AND FOR MY CREW A LITTLE MONEY.

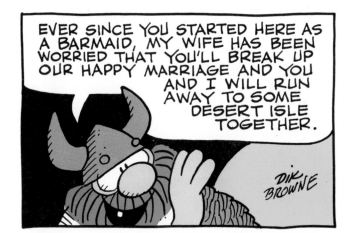

DIK BROWNE - 3-28

Just running down to the local store for some horribly good
cartoon books, colour albums, calendars, diaries, reminder
calendars, greeting cards and giftwrap and tags – all
featuring me of course!

Why not join me before the barbarians get there!

Hagar Books to collect:

POCKET BOOKS
Hagar Tries Again
Hagar Has A Go
Hagar In A Fix
Hagar On The Rampage
Hagar Gets It All
Hagar In The Rough
Hagar Leads The Way
Hagar Takes A Break
Hagar All At Sea
Hagar On Holiday
Hagar Takes Aim
Hagar In A Stew

COLOUR ALBUMS
Hagar Lets Himself Go
Hagar The Hero

COLOUR CARTOON BOOKS
Hagar Tells It Like It Is
Hagar Never Say Die
Hagar Makes An Entrance
Hagar Welcome Home

BLACK + WHITE CARTOON BOOKS
Hagar Meets His Match
Hagar In A Hurry

Hagar The Horrible's Viking Handbook